LANGUAGE ARTS 808
WRITING, LISTENING, AND READING

CONTENTS

Authors:

Carl R. Green, Ph.D.
Brian Jaffe
William R. Sanford, Ph.D.

Editor-in-Chief: Richard W. Wheeler, M.A.Ed.
Editor: Margaret Leech
Consulting Editor: Larry L. Howard, Ed.D.
Revision Editor: Alan Christopherson, M.S.

Alpha Omega Publications®

804 N. 2nd Ave. E., Rock Rapids, IA 51246-1759

WRITING, LISTENING, AND READING

The study of language arts includes four important skills: *reading* and *listening*, to receive information, and *speaking* and *writing*, to express facts, ideas, and feelings to others. In this LIFEPAC® you will study a number of interesting aspects about three of these skills.

First, you will learn about letter writing. You will learn how to write three kinds of business letters and three kinds of personal letters. Knowing how to write good letters is a valuable skill.

Second, you will learn how to develop your listening skills. When people talk, their meaning is usually literal. Sometimes, however, the speaker's words imply what is meant; that is, the meaning must be inferred by the listener. At other times a speaker's meaning can be understood better if the listener recognizes nonverbal language as well as the use of certain figures of speech. Your study of listening will also include tips about how to be a good listener. To be able to listen well is another valuable skill.

Third, you will learn how to intelligently read nonfictional literature, including newspapers and news magazines. You will explore how to distinguish fact from opinion. You will learn that some news is slanted and that statistics can be misleading. You will also learn how to use logical thinking and how to evaluate sources of information. To learn all these skills is worth your time.

OBJECTIVES

Read these objectives. The objectives tell you what you will be able to do when you have successfully completed this LIFEPAC.

When you have finished this LIFEPAC, you should be able to:

1. Explain the structure and form of a business letter.
2. Name and write three kinds of business letters.

3. Explain the structure and form of a personal letter.
4. Name and write three kinds of personal letters.
5. Identify literal meanings.
6. Identify implied meanings.
7. List ways to identify verbal and nonverbal meanings.
8. List the characteristics of a good listener.
9. Distinguish between fiction and nonfiction.
10. Distinguish between fact and opinion.
11. Identify propaganda and slanted news.
12. Explain the importance of using logical thinking and reading.
13. Explain how statistics can be misleading.
14. Evaluate sources of information.
15. Identify the distinctive characteristics of news stories and newspapers.
16. Explain the role of news magazines.
17. Use the spelling and vocabulary words in this LIFEPAC correctly.

Survey the LIFEPAC. Ask yourself some questions about this study. Write your questions here.

_____
_____
_____
_____
_____
_____
_____
_____
_____
_____
_____

I. WRITING LETTERS

The writing skill you will study in this section is letter writing. You will learn how to write both business and personal letters.

Letter writing is an important skill. Much of the New Testament is made up of letters. Many business transactions depend on letters. Letters are written to absent relatives and friends. Letters are sometimes written to strangers, too. Letters can be an important part of your life.

Although the most common way of communicating with one's family and friends is in face-to-face conversation, sometimes writing letters is necessary instead. The ability to write good letters, whether for business or for social reasons, is an asset. When you need to do so, you should be able to write an effective letter using correct **form** and **structure** to convey your message clearly, neatly, and respectfully.

A properly written business letter will leave a favorable impression with the receiver and its message will be taken seriously. A sloppy letter, carelessly written, will make a bad impression—it may even offer an insult to a busy person upon whose time and interest it is making a claim. Remember that a letter is a kind of image of one's self.

Personal letters written to friends should also use correct form and structure. Good letters show that the writers care and that they regard the receivers of their letters as special people. Good letters are fun to receive. The person who receives an enjoyable letter will probably read it more than once. The ability to write good letters is an important adult skill.

In this section you will learn how to write both business and personal letters. You will learn that a letter has a structure (parts) and a form (style). You will learn how to write three kinds of business letters. First, you will learn about a letter that requests an adjustment because a bill you received is wrong. Then, you will study how to order merchandise. Finally, you will find out how to write a letter of application. You will also be taught how to write three kinds of personal letters: friendly letters, letters of invitation, and thank-you letters.

SECTION OBJECTIVES

Review these objectives. When you have completed this section, you should be able to:

1. Explain the structure and form of a business letter.
2. Name and write three kinds of business letters.
3. Explain the structure and form of a personal letter.
4. Name and write three kinds of a personal letters.
17. Use the spelling and vocabulary words in this LIFEPAC correctly.

VOCABULARY

Study these words to enhance your learning success in this section.

acquaintance (u kwān' tuns). A person you know but not a close friend.
addressee (u dre sē'). The person to whom a letter is addressed.
form (fôrm). The way parts are arranged; style.
indent (in dent'). Begin a line farther from the left margin than other lines.
margin (mär' jun). Edge; blank space to the left and to the right of the printing or writing on a page.
salutation (sal yü tā' shun). A greeting; a letter begins with a salutation such as "Dear Sir."
stationery (stā' shu ner ē). Writing materials; paper, cards, and envelopes.
structure (stuk' chur). Anything composed of parts arranged together.
title (tī' tul). The name of a person's occupation, such as "Manager."

Note: All vocabulary words in this LIFEPAC appear in **boldface** print the first time they are used. If you are unsure of the meaning when you are reading, study the definitions given.

Pronunciation Key: hat, āge, cãre, fär; let, ēqual, tėrm; it, īce; hot, ōpen, ôrder; oil; out; cup, pùt, rüle; child; long; thin; /TH/ for then; /zh/ for measure; /u/ represents /a/ in about, /e/ in taken, /i/ in pencil, /o/ in lemon, and /u/ in circus.

3

THE STRUCTURE AND FORM OF BUSINESS LETTERS

Because business letters are so important in almost everyone's life, a person should know how a good letter is put together. What are the parts of a business letter? How are they organized into an effective whole? These questions on **form** and **structure** will be answered in the following paragraphs.

The structure of a business letter refers to the arrangement of the letter's parts. A business letter has six parts. The form of a business letter refers to the letter's style. Although several forms may be considered, this LIFEPAC will discuss only the full block form because it is the most common form used in business today. A business letter consists of these six parts:

1. Heading: The heading includes the writer's address and the date he writes the letter.
2. Inside Address. The inside address includes the name, title, and address of the person or company to whom he is writing.
3. Salutation: The salutation is the greeting that follows the inside address.

   Examples:
   > Dear Sir:
   > Dear Ms. Smith:
   > Gentlemen:

4. Body: The body includes the paragraphs of the letter.
5. Closing: The complimentary close immediately follows the body of the letter and is followed by a comma.

   Examples:
   > Very truly yours,
   > Sincerely,
   > Respectfully,

6. Signature. The signature is the writer's name. It identifies who wrote the letter.

Study the following example and complete the activity.

1.1 Look for the six parts of a business letter in the preceding list. Write a sentence about each part defining it in your own words.

a. _____

b. _____

c. _____

d. _____

e. _____

f. _____

Teacher check _____

Initial   Date

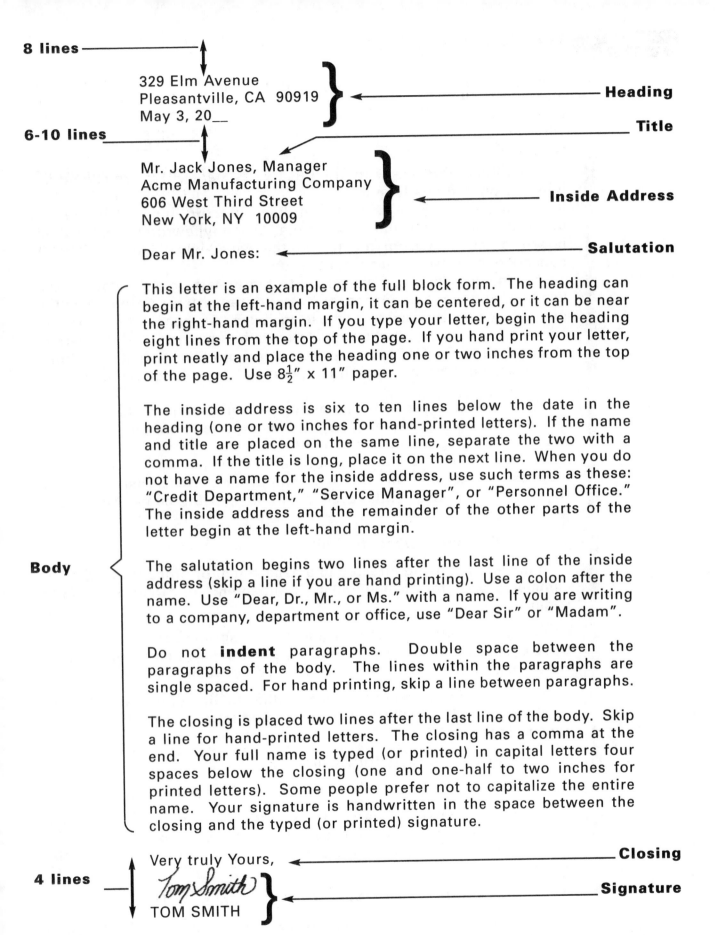

8 lines

329 Elm Avenue
Pleasantville, CA 90919
May 3, 20__

Heading

Title

6-10 lines

Mr. Jack Jones, Manager
Acme Manufacturing Company
606 West Third Street
New York, NY 10009

Inside Address

Dear Mr. Jones: **Salutation**

Body

This letter is an example of the full block form. The heading can begin at the left-hand margin, it can be centered, or it can be near the right-hand margin. If you type your letter, begin the heading eight lines from the top of the page. If you hand print your letter, print neatly and place the heading one or two inches from the top of the page. Use $8\frac{1}{2}$" x 11" paper.

The inside address is six to ten lines below the date in the heading (one or two inches for hand-printed letters). If the name and title are placed on the same line, separate the two with a comma. If the title is long, place it on the next line. When you do not have a name for the inside address, use such terms as these: "Credit Department," "Service Manager", or "Personnel Office." The inside address and the remainder of the other parts of the letter begin at the left-hand margin.

The salutation begins two lines after the last line of the inside address (skip a line if you are hand printing). Use a colon after the name. Use "Dear, Dr., Mr., or Ms." with a name. If you are writing to a company, department or office, use "Dear Sir" or "Madam".

Do not **indent** paragraphs. Double space between the paragraphs of the body. The lines within the paragraphs are single spaced. For hand printing, skip a line between paragraphs.

The closing is placed two lines after the last line of the body. Skip a line for hand-printed letters. The closing has a comma at the end. Your full name is typed (or printed) in capital letters four spaces below the closing (one and one-half to two inches for printed letters). Some people prefer not to capitalize the entire name. Your signature is handwritten in the space between the closing and the typed (or printed) signature.

Very truly Yours, **Closing**

Tom Smith
TOM SMITH **Signature**

4 lines

Complete this activity.

1.2 Make a list of the six parts of a business letter.

a. _____ d. _____

b. _____ e. _____

c. _____ f. _____

Business letters are written on 8½" x 11" paper. Letters should be typed or printed neatly in ink.

The heading can begin at the left-hand **margin**, it can be centered, or it can be near the right-hand margin. When typewritten, the heading begins eight lines from the top of the page; when hand-printed, it appears one or two inches from the top.

The inside address is placed six to ten lines below the date of the heading, or one or two inches for hand-printed letters. As stated on the previous page, the inside address includes the name of the person and/or the company to whom the letter is being written. If the person addressed has a **title**, separate the name from the title with a comma if both are on the same line. If the person's title is long, place it on the next line.

The inside address, the salutation, the paragraphs of the body, the closing, and the signature all begin at the left-hand margin. In the full block form, paragraphs are not indented.

The salutation begins two lines after the last line of the inside address, or after one line if being hand-printed. When using a name, the word "Dear" and a title, such as Mr., Ms., or Dr., comes before and a colon comes after.

Example: Dear Mr. Smith:

If the letter is being directed to a department or office, "Dear Sir:" is commonly used for an individual, "Gentlemen:" or "Dear Sirs:" for a company.

In a typed letter the lines inside the paragraph are single-spaced. Double spacing is usual, however, between each paragraph. In a handwritten letter only one line is skipped between each paragraph.

The closing is placed two lines after the last line of type in the body. Skipping a line is adequate for hand-printed letters. The closing has a comma at the end.

Example: Very truly yours,

Notice that only the first word of the closing is capitalized.

The signature has two parts. The writer's name is typed (or printed) four lines, or one to two inches, below the closing. This part is capitalized, though some people prefer not to capitalize the entire name.

Examples: JOHN W. JACKSON or John W. Jackson

The signature is handwritten between the closing and the typed or printed signature.

 **Answer these questions.** Each answer will have two parts. *Part a* will explain typewritten letters, and *Part b* will explain hand-printed letters.

	Typewritten	**Hand-Printed**

1.3 How far from the top of the page should the heading begin?

a. _____ b. _____

1.4 How far down from the heading should the inside address begin?

a. _____ b. _____

1.5 How far down from the inside address does the salutation begin?

a. _____ b. _____

1.6 What is the distance between paragraphs?

a. _____ b. _____

1.7 How far down after the last line of the body does the closing begin?

a. _____ b. _____

1.8 What is the distance between the closing and the typed (or hand-printed) signature?

a. _____ b. _____

THREE KINDS OF BUSINESS LETTERS

In business, letters are written to handle various transactions: buying, selling, or exchanging; extending credit or courtesy; making, breaking, or amending agreements; submitting applications and sometimes resignations. In ordinary daily life, however, three kinds of business letters are commonly used: the adjustment letter, the letter of order, and the letter of application.

The adjustment letter. Writing an adjustment letter becomes necessary when someone has made an error. Perhaps you ordered some merchandise, and a company sent you the wrong thing. The error might be the price that was charged. The result is this: You have a complaint, and you want an adjustment so that the error will be corrected. Being polite and using tact are important. Your Christian background should show itself in all of life's activities, including business dealings. You are more likely to be treated courteously and efficiently when you, too, are considerate and polite.

What should you do if you were preparing a letter of adjustment? How can you go about organizing its contents so that the information will be clearly stated and the adjustment you wish to be made will occur? Take note of the following suggestions:

Make a list of facts and specifics before you write your letter. Include them in the letter you write. Here is an example of such a list:

a. Address (Credit Department, City Emporium, 1001 First Avenue, Niceville, IL 66061)
b. Purchased a sled, stock #2001a on November 19, 20__
c. The regular price was $29.95. You purchased it on sale for $19.95.

7

d.　The purchase price charged to your account was the regular price rather than the sale price. Account #2204.

　　e.　Request an adjustment for the ten-dollar difference and sales tax on the difference.

　　Now you would be ready to write a business letter requesting an adjustment. You have all the facts and specifics you need. Your letter might look like this one:

429 Magnolia Avenue
Niceville, IL 66061
January 7, 20__

Credit Department
City Emporium
1001 First Avenue
Niceville, IL 66061

Dear Sir or Madam:

On November 19, 20__, I purchased a sled, stock #2001a, from your Sporting Goods Department. The regular price for this merchandise was $29.95. This sled was on sale for $19.95 the day I purchased it.

I charged this purchase to my account with your store. My account number is 2204. When I received my bill this month, I found that the regular price ($29.95) had been charged to my account rather than the sale price ($19.95). I am requesting that my bill be adjusted. Please subtract the ten-dollar ($10.00) difference and the sales tax on this amount.

Sincerely yours,

Alice R. Sanchez

Alice R. Sanchez

Complete this activity.

1.9　Write an adjustment letter on a separate sheet of paper. This letter will be in full block form and will have all six parts that you have studied. Type or print with a pen. Use the following list of facts and specifics:

　　a.　Address:　　Mr. John R. Grissom
　　　　　　　　　　Credit Manager
　　　　　　　　　　Redondo Book Store
　　　　　　　　　　4319 W. 190th Boulevard
　　　　　　　　　　Redondo Beach, CA 90277

b. Purchased a set of encyclopedias, catalog #320887, on April 3, 20__. The encyclopedias were delivered to your residence on April 10, 20__.
c. Volumes 7 and 12 were missing from the shipment.
d. Request an adjustment. You would like to receive the missing volumes. If the missing volumes are not available, you would like to make arrangements to have the encyclopedias returned to the store and the purchase price of $236.54 removed from your account. Your account number is J21104.

When you finish writing this letter, give it to your teacher to check.

Teacher check _____

             Initial   Date

The order letter. The order letter is very much like a letter of request. A letter of request asks for information, a catalog, or a particular piece of literature. Usually no charge or only a small charge is made for the items you request. An order letter, on the other hand, is a way of making a purchase. Always make a list of the items or merchandise you are ordering. All necessary information, such as price, catalog number, size, and model number should be included. Remember to indicate the method of payment: charge, money order, check, or C.O.D. List the prices of the merchandise so that they can easily be added. Add sales tax and shipping charges if you know them.

Study the following example of an order letter and complete the activity.

1149 Euclid Avenue
Irving, TX 77707
October 19, 20__

Ajax Bicycle Company
221225 Main Street
Dallas, TX 75206

Dear Sir or Madam:

An order is submitted for the following replacement parts for my Ajax ten-speed bicycle, Model No. 2 of your lightweight line. The parts and prices are from your current catalog.

1. One 46-inch chain, Catalog #747b (6):	$5.95
2. Two 135 dirt tires, Catalog #165c (4): @ 3.95	7.90
3. One set of handle bars, green, Catalog #444a (9):	.95

Subtotal:	$14.80
Sales Tax:	.90
Total:	$15.70

A money order in the amount of $15.70 is enclosed to pay for this purchase.

Sincerely yours,

Dave L. Morgan

Dave L. Morgan

1.10   Write an order letter. Use a separate sheet of paper. This letter will be in full block form and will have all six parts that you have studied. Type or print with a pen. Use the following information:
a. Address: Same as in the example order letter.
b. Merchandise: One racing seat
                         Two inner tubes, size 135
                         One can of blue touch-up paint
                         Five packages of replacement spokes
Invent your own catalog numbers and prices. Give good descriptions of the merchandise.

When you finish writing this letter, give it to your teacher.

Teacher check _____
                                 Initial   Date

The application letter. The letter of application is used to apply for a job. It is sometimes used to apply for a scholarship or for admission to a school or college. A person writes a letter of application because he wishes to be chosen for something that is important to him. His letter may be one of many letters submitted by people who are competing against him for the same position or opening. Although one does not want to appear conceited, his letter should "sell" him as the person most qualified for the job he is seeking.

As a young adult you may not have had an opportunity to write a letter of application. Nonetheless, the time to learn how to write a letter of this kind is now. You will then be prepared and will feel more confident when you must compose such a letter.

A letter of application should contain some specific information. The first paragraph should state the job for which you are applying. You may also wish to tell how you learned of the opening—especially if someone recommended you.

In the next one or two paragraphs, tell about your qualifications for the job: your age, your education, and your experience. If you have special interests that pertain to the position you are seeking, you can also state what they are. Be careful not to give information about yourself that does not relate to the purpose of your letter.

If appropriate you can give one or two references. The references should name respected people who can say something favorable about your character and ability. Your pastor, principal, and teachers are good examples of people to use for references. Of course, you should request permission to use a person's name before you do so.

The last paragraph of your letter should request an interview. It should also include your telephone number.

Now study the following example of a letter of application:

4718 Oak Lane, Apt. C
Seattle, WA 98104
May 10, 20__

Dr. Mary Silvers
Medical Arts Pharmacy
235 51st Street NW
Seattle, WA 98125

Dear Dr. Silvers:

Dr. Philip Thomas, a physician in the medical building where your pharmacy is located, is a neighbor of mine. He suggested that I write you about an opening you have for a delivery boy. I understand that you are looking for a person my age to deliver prescriptions and to do light maintenance jobs. I also understand that a bicycle is required to deliver the prescriptions.

I am a student at Prince of Peace Christian School. I am thirteen years old and big for my age. My health is excellent, and my school attendance has been perfect this year. I had a paper route for two years, and I assist the groundskeeper at my school. I am a good mathematics student and can work with money.

My bicycle is only one year old. My parents and I purchased it together. They paid half and the other half came from money I earned and saved from my paper route. I have a good understanding of how the streets and addresses run in this part of the city. I am sure I can do a dependable job for you.

The following persons can give you further information about my moral character and ability: (1) Pastor David Johnston, Principal, Prince of Peace Christian School, Seattle, Washington, can be reached by telephone during the day at 377-4228 and (2) Mrs. Helen Thompson is my mathematics teacher. She can be reached at the same phone number after 3:00 p.m. during the week.

If you wish, I can come to your place of business for an interview at your convenience. I can be reached at home by telephone at 372-1010.

Fred R. Roberts

FRED R. ROBERTS

THE FORM OF THE ENVELOPE

Business letters are usually sent in envelopes that are $4\frac{1}{8}$" x $9\frac{1}{2}$" in size. A smaller envelope that is $3\frac{5}{8}$" x $6\frac{3}{8}$" can also be used. The face of the envelope should look similar to this illustration:

Return Address

Thomas Gibbons
429 Michigan Avenue
Farmington, IA 50518

Mr. William Paxton
General Manager
The Staple Corporation
2103 West Third Avenue
Buffalo, NY 14202

Addressee
(same as inside address)

When using the larger of the two envelopes, the letter is folded in thirds:

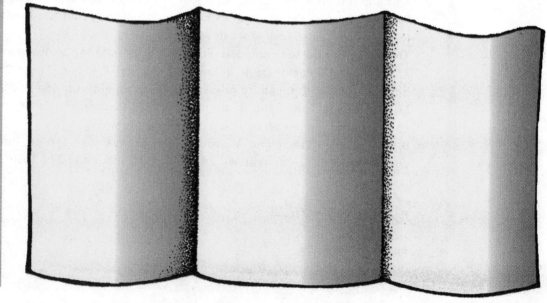

When using the smaller of the two envelopes, the letter is folded in half and then in thirds:

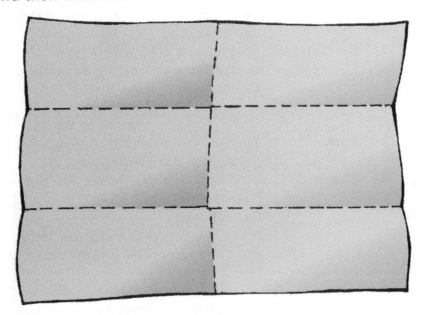

Complete this activity.

1.11 Write a letter of application on a separate sheet of paper. Use all the techniques you have learned. Pretend you are applying for a job as an assistant janitor at a hardware store or as a sales clerk at a department store. Make up the name and address of the store as well as the owner's or manager's name. When you finish, place this letter in an envelope, address the envelope, and turn it in to your teacher.

Teacher check _____

Initial   Date

THE STRUCTURE AND FORM OF PERSONAL LETTERS

The personal letter is the favorite letter for most people. Before studying its three most popular types, you will now examine the structure and form of personal letters.

Structure. A personal letter has five parts. Unlike the business letter, the personal letter does not have the address of the receiver written inside the letter. The other five parts are similar in structure to those of the business letter, but are slightly different in form. As you study the following paragraphs, these similarities and differences will become clear to you.

1. **Heading.** The heading includes your address and the date you write the letter. In personal letters the heading is on the right-hand side of the page and forms the right-hand margin.

2. **Salutation.** Salutations are more friendly in personal letters. The salutation ends with a comma rather than a colon.

   Examples: Dear Bob,
   Dear Mom,
   Dear Aunt Sally,

3. **Body.** The body includes the paragraphs of your letter. The paragraphs are indented.

4. **Closing.** Closings are friendlier in personal letters than in business letters.

   Examples:

   If the person receiving the letter is a family member, the closing can be one of these or something similar.

   Love,
   Affectionately,
   Your brother,
   Your sister,

   For a casual **acquaintance** such closings as these are appropriate:

   Sincerely,
   Sincerely yours,

   For another Christian such closings as these are appropriate:

   Yours in Christ,
   In His Spirit,
   His blessings be with you,

   Note: In any closing the first word is always capitalized as well as any words that refer to God. A comma belongs at the end of the closing. The closing is centered or is placed to the right of center.

5. **Signature.** The writer's signature is either centered below the closing or below the closing and slightly to the right. Only the first name appears in the signature unless for some reason it is necessary to include his full name. The writer's name does not appear in printed form a second time as it does in a business letter.

Form. Personal letters can be typed, but handwriting is generally preferred. When a person is writing in longhand, he should not use lined paper. Tablet paper or special letter **stationery** should be used. Using only one side of a sheet of tablet paper is preferred. One may write on both sides of a sheet of stationery unless the letter is only two pages in length.

For typed personal letters one can use any size paper or stationery. Double space should be allowed between each of the five parts of the personal letter, including the paragraphs of the body. You should sign rather than type your signature.

Handwritten letters begin one-half inch from the top of the paper or stationery. An additional half-inch may be allowed between each of the five parts of the personal letter. If the letter is long, a line can be skipped between paragraphs of the body. Skipping a line between paragraphs is not necessary if the letter is short.

Study the following example. Look for the five parts you have learned about.

Heading

416 Third Street
Los Angeles, CA 91658
April 29, 2001

Salutation

Dear Charlie,

Body

The personal letter does not have an inside address. It does have a heading, a salutation, a body, a closing, and a signature. The form of these parts in a personal letter is different from a business letter.

The heading is on the right-hand side. The salutation ends with a comma rather than a colon. The paragraphs are indented. Your closing is centered or is to the right of center. Your signature contains only your first name and is written below the closing. Do not print your name a second time.

The salutation and closing are friendlier in a personal letter. The five parts are close together.

Closing

Your friend,

Signature

Jack

$\frac{1}{2}$"between each of the five parts

The Personal Letter

Answer these questions.

1.12   What are the five parts of a personal letter?

         a. _____
         b. _____
         c. _____
         d. _____
         e. _____

1.13   Where is the heading of a personal letter placed?

         a. _____
         b. _____

1.14   Do salutations in personal letters end with a colon or a comma?

         _____

1.15   Are the paragraphs of the body in a personal letter indented? _____

1.16   What words are capitalized in the closing of a personal letter?

         _____

1.17   Which punctuation mark is used at the end of a closing?

         _____

1.18   The signature in a personal letter differs in two ways from the signature in a business letter. What are these differences?

         a. _____
         b. _____

1.19   When a personal letter is handwritten, what distance is found between each of the five parts? _____

THREE KINDS OF PERSONAL LETTERS

Personal letters are used for many occasions and purposes. Three kinds of personal letters most commonly used are the friendly letter, letter of invitation, and the thank-you letter.

The friendly letter. The friendly letter will follow the structure and form of the personal letter. The effort to write a good friendly letter becomes difficult when the writer cannot make its content interesting. People write friendly letters to family, relatives, and friends whom they have not seen for some time. Keeping the following ideas in mind can bring the best results to the sincere writer.

First, write more about yourself and other people than about things. Your reader will be more interested in what you are doing and in what has happened to you recently. A new family camper may be exciting to you, but it may not be interesting to your friend.

Second, give some thought to the age of the person who will receive your letter. If you are writing to a person your own age, you could tell about your experiences with a new skateboard. If, on the other hand, you are writing to your grandparents, you might leave out your skateboard experience. It will hardly appeal to them. In fact, it might

16

even cause them to fear for your safety. In general, choose topics that will be suitable to the reader's age and background.

Third, your letters will be more lively and entertaining if you describe an experience in vivid detail, rather than simply making general statements about it or commenting only about your family, friends, and school. You may include general statements of this kind, but do not limit your letters to them.

In your last paragraph you should wish the readers well if you have not already done so. You might also mention that you miss them and hope to hear from them soon.

Complete this activity.

1.20 Write a friendly letter to a relative or friend on tablet paper or stationery. After it has been checked by your teacher, mail your letter. When addressing the envelope, you should use the same rules that apply to addressing envelopes for business letters. No titles, of course, are placed after the addressee's name, but *Mr.* or *Ms.* should be used. On the other hand, you would seldom use *Mr.* or *Ms.* before your own name in the return address.

Teacher check _____

                                     Initial   Date

The invitation. Invitations to parties and to other special events can be purchased at a stationery store or in the stationery supply section of many stores. They can also be made at home. Such colorful notices are useful when large numbers of people are involved.

When one, two, or three people are to be invited to a very special occasion, or when the invitation is for overnight or longer, an invitation in the form of a short personal letter is often sent. Be sure to include the following details:

1. Who will be in attendance, including the chaperons;
2. Any special explanation about the nature of the invitation;
3. The day, date, and time;
4. Your address and telephone number and the address or location of the get-together;
5. Anything special the invited person needs to bring;

Begin with a sentence or two to welcome the person who is being invited. Emphasize this feeling at the end of the letter by stating your hope that your friend will be able to attend, but do not beg.

Letters of invitation follow the same structure and form as the friendly letter, but they are much shorter. One or two paragraphs are a normal length. One may use unlined tablet paper, stationery, or note cards. Either blue or black ink is acceptable.

Complete this activity.

1.21 Write a letter of invitation on a separate sheet of paper. This letter will use the structure and form of a personal letter and will have only one or two paragraphs. Include these details:

1. Pretend you are inviting a friend, who lives sixty miles away, to a weekend in the mountains with your family.
2. If he accepts, explain that your family will pick him up on the way to the mountains; tell him also what to bring, such as a sleeping bag and warm clothing.
3. State the day, date, and time of arrival at his residence and the day, date, and time of return.
4. Be specific about where you will spend the weekend and what you will do.

When you finish, give this letter to your teacher. An addressed envelope is optional.

Teacher check _____

Initial   Date

The thank-you letter. The thank-you letter is really more of a note. Although it has the five parts of a personal letter, it is very short—one paragraph or two. A person writes a thank-you letter for a gift received, for a special favor performed, and for a good time or special treat provided.

Do not say, "Thanks for the present" or "Thank you for the good time." Mention the gift, favor, good time, or special treat by name. The writer should try to make the giver feel that his gift is liked and appreciated.

Promptness is important. Thank-you letters should be sent within a week of receiving the gift, favor, or special treat unless the delay is for a good reason. A late thank-you letter is better than none at all, of course. The following letter is an example of a thank-you letter:

> 4771 Elm Avenue
> Topeka, KA   66117
> November 22, 2001
>
> Dear Mary Ann,
>
>   Thank you and thank your family for inviting me to the mountains last weekend. I had a really nice time, and I especially enjoyed the skiing. The best part of the weekend was being with you and your family. Though we don't see each other as much as we once did, you are still one of my best friends.
>
>   Always your friend,
>   Brenda

Thank-You Letter

Complete this activity.

1.22 Write a thank-you letter using thank-you note card, stationery, or unlined tablet paper. The subject of your thank-you letter can be the sweater your grandmother knitted for you. Give the completed thank-you letter to your teacher. An envelope is optional.

 Teacher check _____

Initial   Date

SPELLING

Study these words in Spelling Words-1. Learning to spell and use these words correctly will help you.

Spelling Words -1

adversary	interest	alien
arrangement	library	assassin
beautiful	nomination	asterisk
buried	pharmacy	bizarre
consequential	forty-five	conference
definitely	relation	comparatively
disguise	shining	conscience
existence	surprise	convenience
gasoline	triumph	courageous
handkerchief	Wednesday	counterfeit

 **Complete this activity.**

1.23 Using a separate sheet of paper, choose twenty of these words and write a sentence for each word. When you finish, give the sentences to your teacher for checking.

 Teacher check _____

Initial   Date

 **Ask your teacher to give you a practice spelling test of Spelling Words -1.** Restudy the words you missed.

 Review the material in this section in preparation for the Self Test. The Self Test will check your mastery of this particular section. The items missed on this Self Test will indicate specific areas where restudy is needed for mastery.

SELF TEST 1

Answer *true* **or** *false* (each answer, 1 point).

1.01 _____ Letters are sometimes sent to people you do not know.

1.02 _____ An invitation is a kind of business letter.

1.03 _____ A business letter has five parts.

1.04 _____ The paragraphs are indented in a personal letter.

1.05 _____ The parts of a business letter begin at the left-hand margin.

1.06 _____ The letter of application is only used to apply for a job.

1.07 _____ The addressee on an envelope for a business letter has the same appearance as the inside address.

1.08 _____ The parts of a personal letter are similar to a business letter but slightly different in form.

1.09 _____ Personal letters should be typed rather than handwritten.

1.010 _____ Thank-you letters are the longest kind of personal letters.

Match these items (each answer, 2 points). You may use an answer more than once.

1.011 _____ The paragraphs in a letter

1.012 _____ Your address and the date a letter was written

1.013 _____ Not found in personal letters

1.014 _____ "Sincerely yours,"

1.015 _____ Appears below the closing

1.016 _____ The name and address of the person being written to

1.017 _____ "Dear Mr. Smith:"

a. closing
b. body
c. heading
d. salutation
e. signature
f. inside address

Complete each statement (each answer, 3 points).

1.018 The form of business letter that you studied in this LIFEPAC is called the _____ form.

1.019 The size of paper used for business letters is _____ .

1.020 The distance from the top of the page that the heading of a hand-printed business letter begins is _____ .

1.021 The distance between each of the parts of a personal letter that has been handwritten is _____ inch.

1.022 The salutation ends with a colon in a _____ letter.

1.023 The salutation ends with a comma in a _____ letter.

Briefly describe the purpose of each kind of letter (each description, 5 points).

1.024 adjustment letter _____

_____

_____

1.025   order letter _____
_____
_____

1.026   letter of application _____
_____

1.027   friendly letter _____
_____

1.028   letter of invitation _____
_____

1.029   thank-you letter _____
_____
_____

Answer this question (this answer, 5 points).

1.030   What is the value of being able to write good letters?
_____
_____
_____
_____
_____
_____
_____
_____

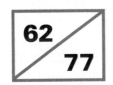

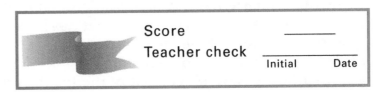

Score _____
Teacher check _____
Initial   Date

Take your spelling test of Spelling Words -1.

II. DEVELOPING LISTENING SKILLS

One of God's many gifts to humanity is the sense of hearing. How great it is to hear the sound of music, the chirping of birds, and the roar of the ocean! Think of some of your favorite sounds. What would life be like without them? A stage play would not be the same if the actors could not be heard, nor would a church service be so inspiring if we could not hear the sermon or the singing. Yes, hearing is a wonderful gift, and being a good listener is a vital skill.

Some people have good listening skills, but others are poor listeners. Those who have poor listening skills are like someone sitting in the end zone at a football game. They cannot see everything that is happening. On the other hand, good listeners are like people sitting in the tenth row on the fifty-yard line. They are aware of everything that happens.

In this section you will learn about listening for literal and implied meanings in speech. You will study such methods of verbal and nonverbal communication as voice tone, gestures, and figures of speech. You will learn the characteristics of a good listener and will use the spelling and vocabulary words in this LIFEPAC correctly.

SECTION OBJECTIVES

Review these objectives. When you have completed this section, you should be able to:

5. Identify literal meanings.
6. Identify implied meanings.
7. List ways to identify verbal and nonverbal meanings.
8. List the characteristics of a good listener.
17. Use the spelling and vocabulary words in this LIFEPAC correctly.

VOCABULARY

Study these words to enhance your learning success in this section.

code words (kōd wurdz). Words that have secret or very special meanings.
conceal (kun sēl'). Hide; keep secret.
dialogue (dī' u log). Conversation.
gesture (jes' chur). Movement of the hands, arms, or other parts of the body; used instead of words, or with words, to help express an idea or feeling.
imply (im plī'). A speaker or writer suggests an idea without expressing it outright or directly.
infer (in fer'). A reader or listener gathers or concludes certain facts from what is read or heard.
literal (lit' ur ul). The exact meaning of words; interpreting words in their usual meaning.
nonverbal (non ver' bul). Communication without using words or by using a minimum of words.
shade (shād). Slightly changing the meaning of a word.
vibration (vī brā' shun). A rapid to and fro motion that produces a sound.

FOUR STEPS IN LISTENING

The act of listening is a process involving four steps: sound, hearing, recognition, and response.

"Marty, did you take out the trash?"

"The trash? Mom, you didn't say anything about the trash."

"I told you at breakfast, just as I've told you a thousand other times; the trash goes out every Wednesday night after supper. You just don't listen!"

Does that conversation sound familiar? You have probably been in Marty's position at one time or another, and you probably have also accused other people of not listening to you. What it comes down to is that people seem to listen, but somehow the words do not get through.

What can be said about the act of listening itself? A scientist would say that listening is actually a four-step process. First, a sound must exist. Sounds are **vibrations** in the air, called sound waves, that the ear can detect. Sound waves must fall in the range of 20 to 20,000 vibrations per second to be heard. This rate of vibrations is called its *frequency*. The sound waves must also have an *intensity*, or *loudness*, if a person is to hear them. Sound engineers measure intensity in decibels. The sound scale starts at 0 for absolute quiet and reaches 140 for a jet takeoff. Decibel levels over 100 can cause physical pain and loss of hearing to the listener. Because many popular bands reach decibel levels of 90 to 130 decibels, hearing experts warn that listeners can suffer permanent hearing loss after prolonged exposure.

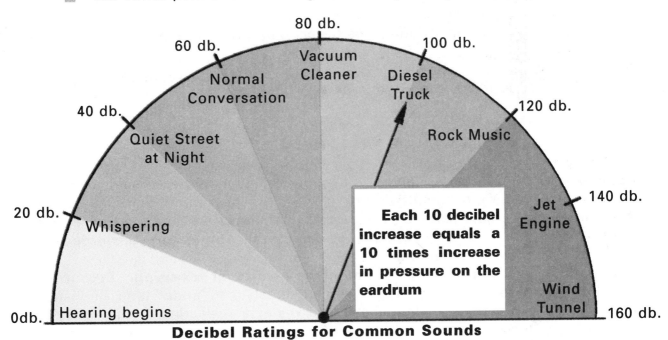

Decibel Ratings for Common Sounds

Second, the sound waves must be picked up and analyzed. This process is called *hearing*. The ear has sensitive inner mechanisms that receive the sound, translate it into electrical impulses, and transmit the impulses to the brain. Since the world is almost never completely silent, such messages are being sent to the human brain every moment of every day.

23

Third, the brain responds to the messages transmitted from the ear. Some sounds, such as the gentle whisper of the wind or the ticking of a clock, are identified and discarded. Other sounds, such as the calling of a name or the screech of brakes, bring a hearer to attention. This sorting out of important and unimportant sounds is called *recognition*.

Fourth and most important, the hearers decide upon a *response* to the sound. Sometimes they do not need to make any response other than to file away the information carried by the sound. At other times the sound alerts them to the need to take immediate action. When Marty is accused of not listening, he has probably "told" his brain not to respond to the sound he was hearing. The readiness to take action is called attention. Young people probably hear almost everything their parents or teachers tell them, but they often turn their *attention* elsewhere. When that happens, they cannot respond to the sound. *Listening, therefore, is the process of paying attention*, whether to a parent's command, a pastor's sermon, or a friend's joke.

Complete these activities.

2.1   List the four steps in listening.

a. _____   c. _____

b. _____   d. _____

2.2   The rate of vibration of a sound is called its _____.

2.3   The loudness or strength of a sound is its _____.

2.4   The brain's willingness to recognize and to respond to a sound is called

_____.

2.5   Levels above _____ decibels can cause permanent injury to a person's hearing.

LISTENING FOR MEANING

To understand the meaning of what is being said, listeners must learn to identify certain clues. They must learn to identify the verbal—worded—clues to **literal**, **implied**, and *figurative* meanings. They must also learn to identify the **nonverbal**—unworded—clues in communication.

Identifying verbal clues to literal meaning. Because you can read this paragraph, you obviously can understand English, one of hundreds of languages and dialects used throughout today's world. You might want to think of reading as a kind of listening—many people say that they hear the words inside their heads as they read. The largest number of messages received each day, however, comes from spoken communications. If you doubt that fact, try going through an entire day without speaking. You will quickly discover how much you rely upon the spoken word to keep in touch with other people.

If you are still not convinced that spoken communications represent a marvelous human accomplishment, read the following sentence: "D'jah gwout las' naht?" If it doesn't make sense, try saying it aloud. The brain will hear those strange sounds and translate them to "Did you go out last night?" If you analyze what people say in everyday conversation, you can find many similar examples. Once the meaning of the question is clear, you can reply, "No, I stayed home to study my Bible lesson," or whatever else is an appropriate answer.

Much conversation involves exchanges of information. Someone says, "Look, it's raining!" or a friend asks you if you are feeling okay. In such situations your natural response is to accept information or question without thinking too much about hidden meanings. Simple exchanges of information rely upon literal meanings. That is, the purpose of the exchange is no more and no less than it seems. That does not mean that everything you hear is correct or proper, just that you immediately know there is no hidden meaning in the statement.

Children, for example, tend to be very literal in their speech. If you look out the window and say, "It's raining cats and dogs," a small child might hurry to see such an odd sight. By now you know that people do not intend that everything they say be taken literally. Les says, "I could disown my brother! He ate the last doughnut." You listen, understand that the crime does not merit extreme punishment, and translate: "I am really annoyed with my brother." A person who tries to attach literal meanings to all speech is often referred to as naive—that is, simple, not sophisticated.

She broke up laughing.

25

How can you be sure that a speaker is dealing only in literal meanings? Experience and long acquaintance with people help. You can also listen for these characteristics of literal meanings:

1. The statement or question deals in facts.
    Example: The river is a mile wide at this point.
2. The statement sounds believable as you understand reality.
    Example: The current is flowing at eight miles an hour.
3. The statement fits the situation.
    Example: "If you don't come in now, you'll miss the beginning of the service."
4. The statement is free from attempts to **shade** meanings, to be poetic, or to be symbolic.
    Example: "Dinner will be cold if you aren't at the table in five minutes."

Most of the time, what people say to you is meant to be taken literally.

Complete these activities.

2.6   Look up these words in a dictionary and write their meaning.
        a. literal _____

        _____

        b. implied _____

        _____

        c. figurative _____

        _____

Complete these statements.

2.7   Literal statements usually deal in _____ .
2.8   The statement should sound _____ .
2.9   The statement fits the _____ .
2.10   The statement should be free from attempts to a. _____ ,
        b. _____ , or c. _____ .
2.11   Most of what people say is intended to be taken _____ .

Identifying verbal clues to implied meaning. As you grow more experienced in dealing with people, you will find yourself better able to understand the meanings behind the words that people use. If communication consisted only of literal meanings, a person need not be concerned about possible hidden meanings. The truth is that everyone sometimes says one thing and means another. To translate those hidden messages, you will have to learn to find the *implied meanings* in what people say.

Two words that might confuse you in this discussion are *imply* and **infer**. The person who is saying more than the literal meaning is *implying* the added idea. The person who receives the message and

LANGUAGE ARTS

ARTS 808

LIFEPAC TEST

83 / 104

Name _____

Date _____

Score _____

LANGUAGE ARTS 808: LIFEPAC TEST

Answer *true* or *false* (each answer, 1 point).

1. _____ Exact meanings are literal.
2. _____ Hidden meanings are inferred.
3. _____ Tone of voice and body language are not the same as non-verbal messages.
4. _____ To be a good listener, you must be able to give good advice.
5. _____ Everything you read in a newspaper is true.
6. _____ Propaganda is usually slanted.
7. _____ Logical thinking requires an open mind.
8. _____ Most statistics are not useful.
9. _____ An autobiography is a primary source of information.
10. _____ A good news story expresses an opinion.

Match these items (each answer, 2 points).

11. _____ requirements of a good listener
12. _____ name and address of the person to whom a letter is sent
13. _____ AP or Reuters
14. _____ knowing size and makeup is important
15. _____ "Dear Sirs:"
16. _____ a willingness to look at both sides of an issue
17. _____ your address and the date
18. _____ The Bible
19. _____ "Your friend,"
20. _____ used to find magazine articles

a. wire services
b. closing
c. heading
d. attentiveness and patience
e. propaganda
f. primary source
g. salutation
h. knowing what is fact and what is opinion
i. *Reader's Guide*
j. inside address
k. statistics

Complete these statements (each answer, 3 points).

21. A figure of speech such as, "He is as strong as an ox," is called a _____ .

22. A figure of speech such as, "Childhood is a summer sun," is called a _____ .

23. When a speaker uses his hands to describe something, his movements are called _____ .

1

24. The process of interpreting the unspoken message in a person's words is called making an _____ .

25. When someone suggests an idea but does not actually state it, she is _____ .

26. When you try to persuade others to believe what you say, good or bad, you are using _____ .

Complete these activities (each part, 2 points).

27. List the six parts of a business letter.
    a. _____
    b. _____
    c. _____
    d. _____
    e. _____
    f. _____

28. List three kinds of business letters.
    a. _____
    b. _____
    c. _____

29. List three kinds of personal letters.
    a. _____
    b. _____
    c. _____

30. List three kinds of meaning determined by verbal clues.
    a. _____
    b. _____
    c. _____

31. List two ways to identify meanings, verbal and nonverbal.
    a. _____
    b. _____

32. List the characteristics of a good listener.
    a. _____
    b. _____
    c. _____
    d. _____
    e. _____
    f. _____

33. Write the address in the proper form. The letter is to be sent to Mrs. Sally R. Hansen, who is the manager of the credit department at Fleming's Department Store. The store is in Hometown, Iowa. The street is 1234 Fourth Avenue. The ZIP code is 54321. The return address has been provided.

Bill Jones
000 Elm Avenue
Hometown, IA 00000

a. _____

b. _____

c. _____

d. _____

e. _____

Take your LIFEPAC Spelling Test

who understands the hidden meaning is *inferring* what is really meant. In other words, Tom must *imply* before Debbie can *infer*.

Social rules often prevent people from saying what they really feel. Politeness may keep you from saying that your aunt's roast was not well cooked. Similarly, kindness may keep you from telling a friend that her dress does not fit well or is in poor taste. Even so, despite your best effort to **conceal** your true meanings, other people often pick up the actual disapproval—just as you would if someone looked at your new jacket and said, "That is an interesting style. I have never seen anything quite like it."

How can you understand or recognize implied meanings? Often the speaker will give one or more clues. The words may not be usual in that situation. You may find yourself responding to a tone of voice or a facial expression. Another kind of clue comes with knowing the speaker's personality. If Robyn, who never complains normally, but today says that she is not feeling well, her mother can infer that she is really ill. By contrast, if Peter usually overstates his aches and pains, his statement that he is "dying from a headache" can be inferred to be a signal that the pain is probably minor.

Another useful method of arriving at implied meanings is to "listen" for what is left unsaid. If Hollis says, "Larry talks too much. He's always popping off behind someone's back," the listener can logically infer that Hollis believes that Larry has been talking *about Hollis* to other people. This relationship between what is said and what is meant, the study of implied meanings, is known as *semantics*. Experts in this field would add, however, that people must be careful not to infer meanings which are not intended. What if, for example, the listener had inferred in the situation above that Hollis actively disliked Larry as a person? It might turn out that Hollis really likes Larry but is upset by this one incident.

People who deal with various types of propaganda—advertising copywriters or political campaign managers, for instance are experts in putting hidden messages into their work. In such cases the words sound acceptable, but the public can easily misunderstand the implied meaning. This technique has been called the use of **code words**. A newspaper, for example, might urge the public to support "law and order" candidates. Careful analysis of the message, however, may reveal that "law and order" can also mean a willingness to trample on some group's civil rights. Similarly, advertising often uses the word "new" as a code word. Printed in large type on the package, it seems to say that the contents have been improved—when actually only the box itself is new.

▶▶▶ **Complete these statements.**

2.12   A person who says more than the literal meaning is _____ more information.

2.13   The person who understands the hidden meaning is _____ what is really meant.

2.14   A person may not say what he feels because of a. _____ or b. _____ .

2.15 Clues that can help you recognize implied meanings include

a. _____

_____ and

b. _____

_____ .

2.16 Two groups of people who use implied meanings are a. _____

and b. _____ .

Identifying verbal clues to figurative meaning. As you increase your skill in recognizing implied meanings, you will begin to notice how people use various *figures of speech*.

Figures of speech are ways of describing things and people by comparing them to other things, people, or ideas. Thus, when someone says, "That Tim is a slave to his job," you know immediately that Tim is a hard worker. You might also infer that the speaker thinks Tim should have more recreation. Figures of speech add color and drama to language, but like any good thing they should not be overdone.

Exaggeration is a common figure of speech. When someone says, "It's hot enough to fry an egg on the sidewalk," everyone understands it as a comment upon how hot the weather is. Most likely, you really do not know if the sidewalk is hot enough to fry an egg or not. People do get tired of using the word *very*, so they use exaggeration to take its place. Exaggeration can be overdone, of course. If you exaggerated everything you say, after a while no one will know what is exaggerated and what is not.

Have you ever said, "He eats like a pig"? Perhaps without knowing it, you were using a *simile*, a figure of speech that compares two things that are basically unlike. The words "like" and "as" help you to recognize similes. "She's mad *as* a wet hen" or "The preacher spoke *like* an angel" would be typical similes. Similes work best when the comparison uses qualities that are well known to both the speaker and the listener.

The *metaphor* is another useful figure of speech. Metaphors give the characteristic or the qualities of one object or person to another unrelated subject. When you say that "the ship plowed through the waves," for example, you are not really suggesting that the ship is an actual plow. The metaphor creates in the listener's mind the picture of a ship cutting through the water as a plow cuts through soil. Be careful about mixing metaphors, however. If you say, "The ship plowed through the waves like a speeding bullet," your listeners will be confused. Ships cannot sail as fast as speeding bullets, nor do bullets "plow" easily through water.

Irony is closely related to sarcasm. Irony uses words to convey a different meaning than the literal meaning would indicate. You might want to think of irony as sarcasm without the intent to injure the feelings of others. For example, you might look at the score and say, "The team has a fat chance." Since the score is 35-0, your listeners will know that their team's chances of winning are quite slim. Sometimes events are considered ironic when they bring the opposite result from that intended. Anyone who has gained weight while dieting knows the irony of such a situation.

Have you ever wanted to point out how ridiculous a situation or person has become? Perhaps you used *satire* to make your point. Satire combines other figures of speech, often with comic effect, to make a point. Writers and speakers may use exaggeration of their subject's mannerisms and gestures—as you might satirize childish behavior by pretending to pout, or throwing a temper tantrum. Sarcasm and irony also work for the satirist. Behavior or situations that you might overlook or ignore become foolish, comic, or stupid when examined in a satiric light. Satire is frequently used to encourage social or political reform. Some satire is gentle and allows the victim to laugh along with the audience. Satire that is harder-edged can be destructive to the person being satirized, however, and should be used with great care.

Now you can see why children take so long to learn how to use language accurately. Are all these "tricks" of language necessary? Sometimes it seems as though life would be simpler if everyone used only literal meanings. If that were the case, spoken communication would be limited and boring. Figures of speech make listening more difficult, but they give you greater freedom to express your emotions and ideas.

Identify the figure of speech described by the statement.

2.17 "She is as mad as a wet hen." _____

2.18 "Idleness is a thief of spare time." _____

2.19 "The sun smiled on the cornfield." _____

2.20 "You look good enough to eat." _____

2.21 "I really needed a flat tire today." _____

2.22 Tom imitates the speech of an ungrammatical speaker to show the need for learning proper speech. _____

Complete this activity.

2.23 Ask your teacher for a copy of a Bible story told in narrative form. As you read the story, pick out the figures of speech. Write each one down and identify it with the proper name. Show the resulting list to your teacher.

Teacher check _____

Initial   Date

Identifying nonverbal clues in voice tone. Thus far, you have learned about the verbal clues to literal meanings, implied meanings, and figurative meanings. Sometimes, you can spot another type of message, which psychologists call a nonverbal message a message delivered without the use of words.

How many times has someone said to you, "Don't use that tone of voice with me?" As you know, the human voice can be more expressive than any musical instrument. It can communicate anger, sorrow, pride and other emotions as surely as do your words. One's voice can also give clues to people about attitudes such as depression, fear, or worry. Machines have been developed that can tell whether you are telling the truth simply by analyzing the amount of stress in your voice.

Tone of voice helps the listener to infer meanings. Parents have many ways of saying a son's or daughter's name. Each time they say only one or two words, but the meanings can range from tenderness to anger. If you wanted to do so, you could make up an entire **dialogue** between two people using only their names.

Complete this activity.

2.24 Study the expressions on the faces of Joe and Patty in the following drawings. Ask a classmate to listen as you say the two names to fit the different situations.

Student check _____

Initial   Date

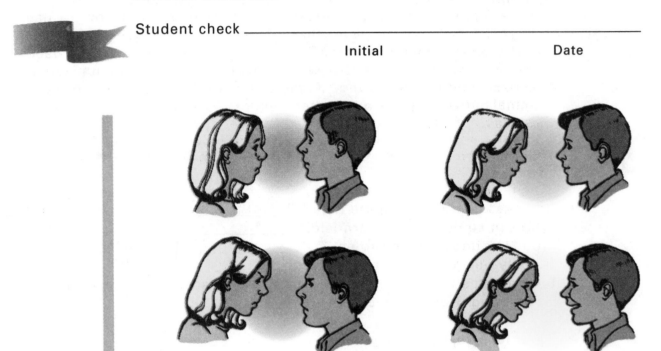

People sometimes speak in a sneering tone of voice, meaning one thing while saying the opposite. The practice is called sarcasm. Sarcasm is used when someone looks out at a rainstorm and says, "It's a lovely day, isn't it?" Similarly, an emphatic tone of voice indicates that the speaker is giving an order: "John, stop that!" A rising note at the end of the sentence indicates that a question is being asked: "What time is it?" Although a printed play can seem dull and lifeless, those same lines spoken by skilled actors can carry a wealth of meaning.

Along with tone of voice, the loudness and pitch–high or low tone–of the voice also carry a message. One old proverb says "an empty wagon makes the most noise." As you may have noticed, people with the least to say seem to chatter the most. If one is sure of himself, on the other hand, he will not need to speak loudly. For example, some teachers speak softly, so that students must listen carefully to hear what is being said. Although custom says that a man's voice should be deep and masculine, Shakespeare wrote that a woman's voice should be "ever soft, gentle, and low." Most of us soon realize that the accent or voice tone does not really tell much about the actual person.

Complete the following statements by describing a message you might infer from the tone or volume of voice described.

2.25 A person who speaks too loudly may be _____ .

2.26 When someone speaks rapidly and the words run together, he or she is probably _____ .

2.27 Someone who speaks loudly and sharply is probably _____ .

2.28 When someone snaps off an answer that means the opposite of what the words say, he is using _____ .

2.29 Love and caring can best be communicated by speaking _____ .

Identifying nonverbal clues in communication. When someone shakes his fist at you, you do not have any difficulty understanding what he means. Such messages are called nonverbal—unworded—messages, and a number of interesting books on that subject have been written.

Some nonverbal messages are obvious. When your grandmother stretches out her arms to say, "Welcome," the gesture she uses is universal. You may also have noticed how a lawyer uses a pointing finger to emphasize a particular point. In this way verbal messages are constantly reinforced by physical actions. Some nationalities—the French and the Italians, for instance—use **gestures** of this type more than others.

Not all nonverbal messages can be decoded easily. For example, how would you interpret Paul's saying, "I really hope you can go with us," if he is holding his hand in front of his mouth at the same time? Some psychologists believe that such gestures indicate that the person is unsure of what is being said or that he may even be lying.

Body posture may also give you a clue to meaning. If you look around your classroom, for instance, you might notice that some students have their arms folded across their chests while the teacher is talking. This posture may indicate a disinterest or a resistance to what is being said. If Roxanne stands with her arms folded or her hands on her hips while talking to you, she may be showing some hostility. Hands on hips may also be a clue that the speaker is impatient. Drumming fingers may suggest the same impatience, whereas nibbling on fingers or pencil can indicate nervousness.

If Bill has crossed his legs away from you, it may mean that he is not interested in what you are saying. If he leans forward, arms open and relaxed, he may be making an extra effort to communicate with you. Eyes are also useful indicators. If Ruth refuses to look directly at you, something may be wrong. A frown, a stare, a rapid blink—all of these actions give clues to disagreement or rejection.

Complete this activity.

2.30 You can find out how good you are at interpreting nonverbal communication. Use a book of photographs, a magazine, or a film strip without the sound. Cover the captions and try to "read" the expressions, gestures, and posture of the people in the pictures. You will probably surprise yourself at how well you do.

Teacher check _____

Initial   Date

Complete these statements. Write on each line the emotion you think would be indicated by the following gestures.

2.31   Mr. Brown is drumming his fingers on the desk. _____

2.32   Coach Hopkins is talking and gesturing with clenched fists. _____

2.33   Mrs. Abbott has her arms across her chest while she listens to the politician. _____

2.34   The witness has his hand in front of his face while testifying about the crime. _____

2.35   The judge is leaning forward in her chair. _____

BEING A GOOD LISTENER

To be a good listener, you must learn about the process of listening, the interpretation of literal and implied meanings, the interpretation of figures of speech, and the evaluation of both tone and body language. Knowing all of this information will make it possible for you to become a good listener, but will not ensure that you will become one. You must also want to be an alert, concerned listener when others speak. One of the biggest complaints heard in American society today is the same one that opened this section: "Nobody listens to me." Children, young people, and adults alike all say that they are being ignored. Sometimes it is because they are separated from family and loved ones. Sometimes it is because big companies and big governments do not seem to listen to people's needs.

Everybody needs someone who will listen to what they have to say. In one college psychology class engineers programmed a computer to respond in certain ways when someone wanted to talk about a personal problem. The machine was not really capable of listening and understanding, but it made the right responses and asked enough general questions at the right time to give that impression. Later, many of the students in the class reported that they felt better for having the chance to talk something out—even with a machine.

Listening is a gift that you can give others. To be a good listener all you have to do is to devote some time to practicing listening skills. Remember the last time you talked about a problem with a sympathetic friend? Perhaps your friend did little more than nod and make encouraging sounds. Even so, you probably felt better afterward just for having put your feelings into words.

This process of allowing someone to open up and talk about personal feelings is called *catharsis*. As a good listener, you will learn that what people need most is an intelligent, interested audience. Most people are not looking for easy answers. In fact, good listeners know that they cannot really solve someone else's problems or take on their burdens. If you can help with a problem, give your friend the advice that you think will work. Do not be disappointed if your advice is not taken. Good listeners know that they are not prized for superhuman wisdom, but for their ability to listen.

Think of the times you have the opportunity to be a good listener. You can visit shut-ins or patients at a convalescent hospital. Almost every day a situation arises where you might say to a friend, "Would it help if you told me about it?" Of course, while you are listening, you will have to practice your listening skills. If you are like most people, you have already mastered many of these skills. As in swimming or soccer, the more you practice skills, the better you will be at using them. The biggest hurdle will be overcoming your own tendency to concentrate on yourself. Many people do not hear what others are saying because they are too busy thinking about their own response.

Listening is a two-way street. When you listen well, others are more likely to listen to you. Listening is a kind of giving of yourself. If you would not hesitate to give your interest, sympathy, time and love to other people, you will not hesitate to give your listening skills.

The Bible speaks about people who lack the maturity to be good listeners in Psalm 135:17: "They have ears, but they hear not . . ." You might want to identify yourself, instead, with Romans 10:17 and 18: "So then faith cometh by hearing, and hearing by the word of God. But I say, Have they not heard? Yes, verily, their sound went into all the earth, and their words unto the ends of the world."

The poet, Jean Ingelow, summed up the tragedy that befalls people who lack good listeners when she wrote:

> Man dwells apart, though not alone,
> He walks among his peers unread;
> The best of thoughts which he hath known
> For lack of listeners are not said.

Are you already a good listener, or do you plan to become one?

Complete these activities

2.36   List the characteristics of a good listener.

       a. _____

       b. _____

       c. _____

       d. _____

       e. _____

       f. _____

2.37   Make a point of using active, creative listening skills for the next twenty-four hours. Afterward, think about your experience. Did you have any trouble concentrating on what others were saying? Were your friends and family aware of your greater involvement in what they were saying? How did you feel about the experience? Write the results of your listening exercise on a separate sheet of paper. When finished, show your essay to your teacher.

Teacher check _____

                         Initial   Date

SPELLING

Study these words from Spelling Words-2. Learning to spell and use these words correctly will help you.

Spelling Words - 2

sew	their	medal
sow	they're	metal
so	vain	meddle
scent	vane	to
sent	vein	two
cent	aisle	too
sight	isle	ascent
site	I'll	assent
cite	pore	chord
there	pour	cord

Complete this activity.

2.38   Using a separate sheet of paper, choose twenty of these words and write a sentence for each word. When you finish, give the sentences to your teacher for checking.

Teacher check _____

                         Initial   Date

Ask your teacher to give you a practice spelling test of Spelling Words -2. Restudy the words you missed.

Review the material in this section in preparation for the Self Test. This Self Test will check your mastery of this particular section as well as your knowledge of the previous section.

SELF TEST 2

Answer *true* **or** *false* (each answer, 1 point).

2.01	_____	Decibel levels over 100 can cause loss of hearing.
2.02	_____	The loudness of a sound is its frequency.
2.03	_____	Literal meanings have hidden messages.
2.04	_____	A speaker's facial expression can add a different meaning to his words.
2.05	_____	A speaker's tone of voice helps you to infer meanings.
2.06	_____	Body posture is an example of nonverbal language.
2.07	_____	A simile is an example of nonverbal communication.
2.08	_____	Salutations in personal letters end with a colon.
2.09	_____	An addressee is the person to whom the letter is sent.
2.010	_____	In a business letter the signature has two parts.

Match these items. You may use each answer more than once (each answer, 2 points).

2.011	_____	"She eats like a bird."	a. exaggeration
2.012	_____	"Thanks, I needed that." (opposite meaning)	b. simile
			c. metaphor
2.013	_____	"I've told you twenty times not to do that!"	d. irony
			e. satire
2.014	_____	Sally imitates the way a sloppy person eats spaghetti to show that good table manners are desired.	
2.015	_____	"The winds howled and groaned."	
2.016	_____	compare one thing with another	
2.017	_____	show how ridiculous a particular situation in government has become	
2.018	_____	overstates a situation	
2.019	_____	describes the qualities of one object that is unrelated to another object	
2.020	_____	often means the opposite of what was actually said	

The salutation and the signature are two parts of a business letter. Write the other four parts (each answer, 4 points).

2.021 _____

2.022 _____

2.023 _____

2.024 _____

Which of the six parts of a business letter is *not* **found in a personal letter9** (this answer, 4 points)

2.025 _____

Write a word that describes each behavior (each answer, 3 points).

2.026 Jack blinks his eyes rapidly and wiggles his foot.

_____

2.027 Jack leans forward to hear better. _____

2.028 Jack folds his arms. _____

2.029 Jack's lips are tight and his hands are clenched in a tight fist. _____

_____

2.030 Jack looks at his feet while speaking. _____

Write the correct word that describes each behavior (each answer, 3 points).

2.031 Janet is speaking too much and too loudly. She is probably _____

_____ .

2.032 Janet orders her sister not to touch her glass collection. She is

probably _____ .

2.033 Janet speaks sharply and loudly to her sister. She is probably

_____ .

2.034 Janet tells her sister how much she loves her. _____

2.035 Janet tells her sister, "Thank you so much for using the last of the

shampoo." _____

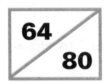

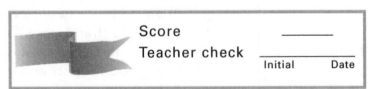

Score _____

Teacher check _____

Initial   Date

Take your test of Spelling Words-2.

III. READING NONFICTION

Nonfiction, or factual, reading material includes books, magazines, and newspapers. In this LIFEPAC you will learn how to read nonfiction intelligently. To read nonfiction intelligently, you must be able to tell what is true from what is false and what is fact from what is opinion. You will learn how to avoid being fooled by what you read. You will study some interesting and useful information about how to evaluate nonfiction. When you learn to do these things, you will have become a mature reader.

SECTION OBJECTIVES

Review these objectives. When you have completed this section, you should be able to:

9. Distinguish between fiction and nonfiction.
10. Distinguish between fact and opinion.
11. Identify propaganda and slanted news.
12. Explain the importance of using logical thinking and reading.
13. Explain how statistics can be misleading.
14. Evaluate sources of information.
15. Identify the distinctive characteristics of news stories and newspapers.
16. Explain the role of news magazines.
17. Use the spelling and vocabulary words in this LIFEPAC correctly.

VOCABULARY

Study these words to enhance your learning success in this section.

apprise (u prīz'). Inform; notify.
editorial (ed u tôr ē ul). An article in a newspaper that expresses an opinion.
logical (loj' u kul). Correct reasoning or thinking; reasonably expected.
reliance (ri lī' uns). Placing trust or confidence in someone or something.
source (sôrs). Place from which anything comes or is obtained; person or book that
    provides information.
viewpoint (vyü' point). Attitude; point of view; outlook.

DISTINGUISHING BETWEEN NONFICTION AND FICTION

The primary purpose of nonfiction literature is to inform, to explain, to define, to analyze, to interpret, or to persuade. Unlike fiction, which is imaginative and whose first purpose is to entertain, nonfiction deals with facts. It also deals with opinion based upon facts.

Nonfictional works of literature include books, magazines, and newspapers. They are concerned with real persons, places, things, ideas, and inventions. Biography, history, science, language, technology, business, philosophy, and religion also belong to the realm of nonfiction.

Readers of such subjects are seeking information or knowledge about these fields. Sometimes they also are interested in learning the opinions that other people, especially authorities in the subject, have about them.

Fiction, on the other hand, deals with imagination and fantasy. The novel, the poem, the short story, and the play, deal with imaginary people in an imagined time and place, living out the meaning of their imaginary lives.

The fiction writer is not appealing primarily to the reason and judgment of readers, but to their feelings and their emotions. At its best, fiction enlarges the world of human experiences and widens its horizons. Even though many factual details may be involved in a piece of fictional writing, the fiction writer's purpose is to entertain, to amuse, or to stir the heart. In so doing the writer frequently appeals for a response of pity, goodness, love, fear, terror, reverence, pride, or compassion.

Writers of nonfiction also try to interest the reader. They try to write with clear, graphic, significant details, but always keep in mind their purpose—to present the facts so that the reader may understand the situation. They do not allow their concern for style to distort facts nor do they draw unsound opinions or evaluations from them.

Answer *true* **or** *false*.

3.1	_____	Nonfiction deals with facts.
3.2	_____	Several important purposes of fiction include attempting to inform, to analyze, to amuse, and to entertain.
3.3	_____	Fiction is imaginative in nature.
3.4	_____	The novel is fiction.
3.5	_____	Plays and history are nonfiction.
3.6	_____	*The World Book Encyclopedia* is nonfiction.
3.7	_____	A writer of nonfiction appeals mostly to the reader's feelings and emotions.

DISTINGUISHING BETWEEN FACT AND OPINION

Before you can become a proficient reader of nonfiction, you must be able to distinguish between what is factual (real or certain) and what is thought to be factual (what is an opinion). A fact is something that exists or has existed; is happening or has happened. For example, that Phoenix is the capital of Arizona is a fact. A fact is based on absolute certainty. That our calendar lists thirty-one days in January is a fact. If Andrew says that January has only thirty days or that Prescott is the capital of Arizona, he is mistaken. His evaluation is not based on a verified fact. Opinion, then, is based neither on absolute certainty nor positive knowledge, but on what *seems* to be true, valid, probable, or likely. If people's facts are right and if their reasoning process is logical, their opinions are probably sound.

To be able to distinguish between fact and opinion, you must know the difference between the two concepts. You should also be able to judge whether or not the facts have been interpreted and evaluated correctly.

Do you have any friends who believe just about everything they hear or read? Putting trust in the printed word is natural. Almost everyone at times backs an argument by saying, "I saw it in the paper," or "I read it in a book." The printed word does have tremendous power. People tend to believe what they read. Should they? Much of what you read is as true as the writer can make it. However, human memories sometimes make mistakes, and the human desire to make a point sometimes carries writers away from the truth. Therefore, the best position to take is that not everything you read is true or free from all error. Consider the source.

When you are reading a Bible story, you know it is true because God's Word is true. When Noah built the ark in answer to God's direction, he did so even though he was living in desert land where a flood was difficult to envision. He believed the truth of God's word. The Bible records that Noah did the right thing. The Flood did come, and Noah and his family survived, as well as all those creatures they took with them in the ark.

 **Complete this activity.**

3.8 Read the account of the Deluge in Genesis (chapters 6–8); then read the account of the Deluge in *The World Book*. Are these accounts different? In what ways? Write a paragraph on a separate piece of paper, explaining why. Use your Christian point of view. When you have finished, show the paper to your teacher.

 Teacher check _____

　　　　　　　　　　　　　　　　Initial　　　　　　　　　　Date

Can you trust your emotions? Many people want to believe in an idea because it is exciting. People like to have exciting things happen to them.

Newspapers, in fact, are criticized for not printing the good things that happen every day. If someone robs a bank, that event is news, and it makes headlines. However, few people find it interesting to read a story about how the bank has not been held up for over fifteen years. Perhaps newspapers print sensational stories for the same reason—to catch people's interest, not to report scientific fact.

One unexplained subject of several news stories over the past few years is Big Foot, an ape-like creature whose appearances have been reported in the northwestern part of the United States and in Canada.

Once you accept the idea that everything in print may not be true, you are ready to examine the evidence for and against Big Foot.

Answer each question with *yes* **or** *no.*

3.9	_____	At least one member of my family has seen a giant animal like Big Foot.
3.10	_____	Unknown giant animals may exist, but I am not sure.
3.11	_____	If giant animals existed, we would already know about them.
3.12	_____	I would like to read more about Big Foot before deciding whether it exists.
3.13	_____	I believe Big Foot exists; the newspaper stories cannot be ignored.
3.14	_____	According to science, Big Foot could not possibly have appeared in California.
3.15	_____	Giant ape-like animals do exist; science fiction has written about them for years.
3.16	_____	People who claim to have seen Big Foot have not always been reliable witnesses.
3.17	_____	Most sightings of giant animals have turned out to be mistakes or hoaxes.
3.18	_____	The total evidence about Big Foot leaves much room for doubt.

Now total your score. Give yourself five points for each odd-numbered (3.9, 3.11, 3.13, 3.15, 3.17) question to which you answer *yes*; do not give any points for a *no* response. Then subtract five points for each *yes* answer to an even-numbered question (3.10, 3.12, 3.14, 3.16, 3.18). Check your score against the following chart:

20-25	You have very definite ideas about giant ape-like animals and probably are not open to careful consideration of the evidence.
10-15	You may have made up your mind too soon. Think about the evidence on both sides of the issue.
0-5	You lean toward believing in giant animals, but you are still open to more careful study of the evidence.
-5 to -10	You have an open mind, along with some curiosity about Big Foot. You are probably waiting for better evidence than you have seen so far.
-10 to -25	You have a skeptical attitude about the entire subject of Big Foot.

 **Complete this activity.**

3.19   Ask ten people the questions, "Do you believe in large ape-like animals such as Big Foot? Why or why not?" Record their answers. Organize your data and write a short paper about people's willingness to believe in sensational subjects. Show the paper to your teacher.

 Teacher check _____

Initial   Date

40

Identifying propaganda and slanted news. Do you remember the definition for *propaganda*? Select the propaganda message from the following items: (1) An advertisement for toothpaste that will "give you a winning smile." (2) A newspaper survey that points out poor conditions at the county jail. (3) A speech by a politician telling why people should vote for new taxes. (4) Your own list of arguments for a larger allowance.

If you said, "All of these statements are examples of propaganda," you would be correct. Any type of information designed to convince or to persuade someone to change his or her behavior is propaganda. Adolf Hitler thought propaganda was so important that he made his Minister of Propaganda one of his government's most important members. Propaganda is neither good nor bad. Propaganda only becomes morally wrong when it uses distortion or untruth, even in support of desirable ends. People usually can recognize truth when they hear it, particularly when they take the time to examine the facts before they draw their conclusions.

The *media*—newspapers, news magazines, radio, and television— have developed a number of ways of using propaganda to "sell" both products and ideas. One typical method of "selling" ideas is known as *slanting*. By choosing only those arguments and facts that support their position, the editors can make their readers believe what they want them to believe. Would you be misled by slanted news? Look at the following example before you answer:

Imagine that you have just walked into a small restaurant. The waiter hands you a menu. As you look down the list of dinners, you spot this item: DEAD COW. FLESH OF ANIMAL THAT DIED LAST WEEK. OUTER SURFACE BURNED. ALMOST RAW IN MIDDLE. $14.95.

How does your appetite react to that "slanted" menu presentation? Of course, the same item could be described in more appetizing terms: JUICY STEAK. WELL-AGED U.S. CHOICE BEEF. BROILED MEDIUM-RARE. Now you are more interested, of course, and rightfully so. Slanting also takes place when the writer or editor "buries" a story in the back of the newspaper or gives little time to it. A newspaper that supports a clean environment would run a story about automobile pollution on the front page. However, a newspaper that supports industrial interests would either ignore the story or print it on back pages where fewer people would read it.

Apply logical thinking. You will not fall victim to false propaganda if you are willing to apply **logical** thinking to what you read and hear. Many arguments that sound logical do not stand up to close examination: "Writers have reported about Big Foot for years in newspapers and magazines. Newspapers only write about things that are real. Therefore, Big Foot is real." That sounds rather logical, does it not? Remember, however, that *newspaper articles are not really about giant animals. The articles are about people who say that they have seen them.* Thus, your job is to decide whether or not to believe these people. The fact that the newspaper or magazine lends its pages to reporting the existence of Big Foot should not influence your thinking.

Complete this activity.

3.20 Using the following details, write two separate paragraphs on a sheet of your own paper. Slant the first paragraph toward belief in Big Foot. Slant the second paragraph against belief in Big Foot. Use any propaganda technique that you think will work. Here are some details to use in developing your paper:

A pair of hunters report seeing a giant animal in the mountains of northern California. They describe it as being ten feet tall, shaggy, and dark in color. They say it walks upright. Both hunters trailed it into a woods where it disappeared. They have tracked it by following the huge footprints that other people have reported. No other animal tracks known to science makes these.

When you have finished this activity, show the paragraph to your teacher.

Teacher check _____

　　　　　　　　　　　　　　　　Initial　　　　　　　　　　　Date

DEALING WITH STATISTICS

Perhaps you have heard the old saying, "Figures lie, and liars figure." In a scientific age people do tend to place great **reliance** on *statistics*—numerical data that sound scientific, reliable, and unarguable. There are many reasons you might distrust statistics, even when the numbers themselves are true. For instance, you might be impressed about the strength of religious feeling in a small town if you saw the statement, "Eighty-five percent of all church members in Podunk attend church every Sunday." However, think about what is missing. Did the statement tell what percentage of the town's population is affiliated with a church? You cannot make a judgment about the strength of religion in that town until you know all the facts about the *size* of the group being discussed.

Similarly, you might read this statement: "Seventy-four percent of those questioned stated that they believe in Big Foot." If that statistic came from a study in which a thousand households were called at random, it would mean that people in the United States probably do believe in such giant animals. What if the people questioned were all in attendance at a convention of science fiction fans? Only people who already have made up their minds would be likely to attend such meetings. Therefore, before you can judge statistics, you also need to know the *makeup* of the subjects who provided the data.

Statistics can also be influenced by the way the question is asked. Think about this data: "Ninety percent of the eighth-grade students surveyed said they would attend school on Saturday." Can you believe that? However, if you know that the student had been asked the following question: "Would you be willing to attend school every Saturday for a month to earn a trip to Disneyland?" Under those conditions, even 90 percent looks low!

Sometimes a statistic will slip by before you have a chance to examine its significance. A publicist for a sports field might say, for example, that the field has a safety record of 99.8 percent for its spectators. You should look at the *true meaning* of that figure. It tells you that attendance there is unsafe for 0.2 percent—and that figures out to 100 injuries in a crowd of 50,000 for a football game. Safety experts would consider that figure unacceptable.

Statistics also can give misleading impressions when they stand by themselves. An advertisement for a cold remedy might tell you that 90 percent of all doctors prescribe its "chief ingredient." The statistic is meaningless because it does not tell you what percentage of doctors prescribe that particular product—if any! Similarly, an ad that tells you that the Jetfire 6 has been rated at 20.8 miles per gallon has meaning only in comparison with cars of a similar size. As you can see, statistics must be *compared* with as much related information as possible before you make a judgment.

Only when you learn to apply these techniques to the statistical data you find in advertisements, articles, and announcements over the airwaves will you be able to use statistical information intelligently.

Complete these statements. What information is missing from these statistics?

3.21 "Flippo soap is 99.44 percent pure." Its _____ is that the soap is 0.56 cent impure.

3.22 "New diet Chocola has 30 percent fewer calories." By making a _____ with other brands, you can decide just how many calories Chocola has.

3.23 "Three out of five athletes wear Everlast jeans." Is the ad talking about all athletes, or only a few? You need to know the _____ of the sample being used.

3.24 "Nine out of ten voters favor lowering property taxes." To judge the truth of this statement, you need to know how the _____ was phrased and under what conditions it was asked.

3.25 "The senator received fifteen letters against the bill." To know if this statistic is important, you first need to know the _____ of the senator's mail—how many letters are usually received, how many were for the bill, and so on.

Complete this activity.

3.26 Clip ten ads from newspapers and magazines that use statistics to sell a product. Mount each ad on a piece of paper and write an analysis of the use—or misuse—of statistics by the copywriter. Draw a conclusion for each one as to whether the statistics were used fairly. Show the completed work to your teacher.

Teacher check _____

Initial   Date

EVALUATING SOURCES OF INFORMATION

One of the most important jobs a student learns is to do research. If you are going to write a paper on automobile pollution, you must find information on that topic. Even more important, you will need to make a judgment about the usefulness of the various **sources** available to you. As an adult you will still be collecting data. Adults do not often write papers for school, but they do need information on everything from buying a house to choosing the right brand of orange juice. Younger students often depend almost entirely upon encyclopedias for their research information. Other sources do exist.

What book should I choose?

Primary sources. The best way to find out about an event is to look for the writings of people who were directly involved in the subject. Books, articles, films, and tape recordings of this type are known as *primary sources*. Typical primary sources include eyewitness reports, autobiographies, memoirs, diaries, letters, newsreel footage, interviews, and other historical records by people who actually participated in the event being studied. The information found in primary sources is not always true, of course. Eyewitnesses make errors, and a general might only tell his side of the battle. Using such sources gives a colorful, firsthand look at the subject, but researchers cannot stop after consulting a single source. To ensure that they obtain a balanced viewpoint, they try to find several primary sources.

Secondary sources. Checking through primary sources takes time. Historians, reporters, and other writers often do this task for you. If you want to study the Vikings, for example, you can probably find out what you need to know by reading several books on that topic. Generally called *secondary sources*, these books are written by persons who were neither participants nor eyewitnesses. The better secondary sources show their scholarly background. A good work on the Vikings footnotes the sources used in each chapter, and will print a complete listing of all sources in a bibliography at the end of the book. Secondary sources are useful to the researcher, but they may be limited by the fact that most are written long after the event took place. Also, do not forget that the author of a secondary source may have a particular viewpoint to sell. Two books on the Vikings, each using the same primary sources, may present opposite views. This type of conflict indicates a problem known as *bias*, or slant. Whom can you believe? A good way to decide is to consult a third source. The most popular interpretation will generally be the more accurate.

Reference materials. The third useful category of nonfiction information is referred to as *reference materials*. This category includes many different kinds of publications. You are already familiar with the more common reference materials: atlases, which provide detailed maps and statistical data on geography; encyclopedias, which compile brief articles on all types of subjects for quick and ready reference; dictionaries, which help you define, spell, and study the history of specific words; general works of statistics and records, such as the *Guinness Book of World Records*; and almanacs, which collect up-to-date summaries of useful statistical and historical information. Most libraries shelve the reference works in a separate location. These sources let you look up specific information quickly, but they rarely treat the topic in depth.

General sources. A fourth category of research information can be found in *general sources*. School textbooks fit into this group; a great deal of information must be presented in a few pages. Most general sources are written for the interests and reading level of a particular age group. Most of these sources present a general **viewpoint** without trying to promote one side of a controversial topic over another. Useful as they are, these books usually leave out many of the complex details that make history come alive.

In summary, reading nonfiction and doing research is like peeling an onion. Every time you strip off one layer, you find another new, untouched layer waiting for you. As you peel each layer you must evaluate the source: Is it reliable? Did the author do a good job of research? What kind of source is it?

 **Complete these statements.**

3.27   Books and articles written by participants and eyewitnesses are called _____ sources.

3.28   Atlases, almanacs, and encyclopedias are known as _____ sources.

3.29   Most history textbooks would be _____ sources.

3.30   A book written about a particular event or subject by an author who did not take part is probably a _____ source.

 Complete the following items by putting the proper number after the title.

         1   for primary source
         2   for secondary source
         3   for a reference source
         4   for a general source

a. *Hammond's Historical Atlas*.............................. _____
b. *U.S. History for Eighth Graders*..................... _____
c. *I Saw Pearl Harbor Bombed*......................... _____
d. *Two Centuries of Roman Life*....................... _____
e. *Information Please Almanac*........................ _____
f. *My Life on the Stage*.............................. _____
g. *The Life of Robert E. Lee*.......................... _____
h. *Western Civilization Through the Ages*............. _____

READING THE NEWSPAPER

As a form of nonfiction, newspapers are intended by their publishers to **apprise** the general public about the facts of the day: *who*, *what*, *when*, *where*, *why*, and *how* things are happening in the world. The story in the newspaper that informs people of a threatened flood or of the scores of last night's basketball game, or of the election of a president or a city manager is informing readers of the facts. Knowing the purpose of the news, then, can help you read your paper more intelligently.

Gorbachev Takes Aim at Yeltsin, Urges Elections

By SONNI EFRON
TIMES STAFF WRITER

Moscow—In a sign of how far Boris N. Yeltsin's star has fallen, his old nemesis, Mikhail S. Gorbachev, rose from the Soviet political graveyard Wednesday to warn the West that Russia is backsliding on democratic freedom and economic reform.

Sounding like a presidential candidate, himself, Gorbachev blamed President Yeltsin for leading Russia "from coup to coup" into the bloodshed of Chechnya. In a speech to Western executives, the former Soviet leader said that only early elections can rescue Russia from crisis.

Gorbachev's attack was one note in a growing chorus of condemnation of Yeltsin, whose popularity and credibility—as well as the national currency—have been driven to new lows by the 2 month-old war in Chechnya.

Today, Yeltsin will try to steady his staggering presidency when he delivers his annual address to Parliament, reassuring disillusioned Russians and a skeptical West that he is still the "main engine and guarantor" of reform, as Foreign Minister Andrei V. Kozyrev put it.

The president may also distance himself from the military bungling and brutality in Chechnya and call for long-delayed reform of the armed forces.

Kremlin aides told the Itar-Tass news agency that Yeltsin will go even further and admit that the military has violated human rights in Chechnya. That report could not be confirmed, however.

Los Angeles Times, Thursday, Feb. 16, 1995 (Los Angeles, CA)

Can you find the Who, What, When, Where, and Why in this news story?

Newspapers publish more than straight news stories. In the editorial section of a newspaper you will find columns expressing the opinions of its editors and those of guest columnists. You will find letters to the editors, poetry by local contributors, and cartoons that comment on the news. In other sections you will find sports articles, reviews of cultural and entertainment activities, and fashion forecasts.

Although less than half of the population reads a daily paper, the reason is not that they have too few papers from which to choose. Over two thousand newspapers are published daily, not counting the free advertising papers and small town weekly papers. These papers, large and small, can be very useful to anyone who wants to be an informed citizen.

News stories. Unless you read a large city newspaper, the chances are that most of the national and international news stories on the front page are written by a handful of large news-gathering agencies called *wire services.* Two of the largest services are Associated Press (AP) and Reuters. You will see those names at the beginning of the story, which often includes the name of the city where the event occurred. Some large newspapers, such as the *New York Times* and the *Los Angeles Times*, maintain their own network of news sources and sell articles to subscribing newspapers. Wire services make it possible for smaller newspapers to run the same "hot" news stories as the large papers with their larger staffs and budgets.

If a local reporter wrote the story, his or her name will probably appear just beneath the headline for the article. This identification of the writer is called a *byline.* When you are evaluating a news story, it helps to know whether it is of local or national origin and who wrote it.

All good news stories stick to the facts. Reporters learn to include the five *W's* and one *H* in their stories: *Who, What, When, Where, Why,* and *How.* Whenever possible, these facts should appear in the first paragraph, called the *lead.* Writing interesting stories while also including all the facts is one of the hardest jobs a reporter must learn.

One of a newspaper's most important rules is that front-page news should not slant or distort the facts. The opinion of both the newspaper owners and reporters should not be apparent in the news coverage. This rule does not mean that a newspaper cannot hold opinions. The First Amendment to the Constitution guarantees freedom of the press, and most newspaper people believe that they have a responsibility to present their views on important issues to the public. Most papers restrict these opinions to the **editorial** page. There you will find the comments and viewpoints of the newspaper, often written in strong, vigorous language.

Suppose the hunters' experience with Big Foot became known. The local paper would probably print a front page news story about the incident giving only the facts as reported by the hunters and other witnesses, if any. If the newspaper then wanted to comment about the dangers of imagining such events, it would use the editorial page to get that viewpoint across. As a newspaper reader, you must be sure to observe whether your paper keeps factual stories separate from articles that contain opinion. That task is not always easy, especially when a newspaper slants a story or does not report it at all.

Complete these statements.

3.32 The name of the reporter who writes a story can be found in the

_____ .

3.33 The names AP or Reuters in the dateline tell you that the story was written by a _____ .

3.34 A good news story contains the five *W*'s and one *H*. The letters stand for

_____ .

3.35 If you want to know a newspaper's position on a local political issue, look on the _____ page.

3.36 A newspaper's right to print the news and to voice its opinions without interference is guaranteed by the _____ .

Special features. Many of the stories that appear in your newspaper should not be called "news." They are called special *features*, and they can be printed today or next week without losing their value. The *comic strips* and *cartoons* are typical features of the newspaper. Other features include recipes, fashion information, and advice columns. Most features appear in many newspapers on the same day, a service known as *syndication*. An important syndicated feature is the paper's *editorial cartoon*, which is usually found on the editorial page. These cartoons may make you smile, but their chief purpose is to make you think about an important social or political issue.

Most newspapers also print *tabulated materials*. These useful items include weather reports and predictions, tide tables, temperature readings from around the world, sports results, death notices, and similar items. If the paper has extra space to fill, short items called *fillers* are dropped in. These items, which may be only three lines long or may run several inches in length, fill up the unsold space around advertisements. You will find that fillers can be quite informative at times, especially if you like unusual facts and humorous aspects of the news.

Advertising. Advertising provides the major income of a newspaper. The amount you pay for a paper often covers only a fraction of the cost of writing, printing, and delivering it. Advertisers buy space to tell you about their services or products, and the cost of the ads pays for the newspaper. At times advertising can be a nuisance, but some ads give you needed information. You would never know about the sale at the record shop, for example, without advertising. The amount you pay for a newspaper could be doubled if the advertising did not pick up the difference.

You may not be a regular newspaper reader now, except for the sports and features. However, if you want to be an informed citizen, ready to speak for and to support Christian causes, you will need to know what is going on around you. Only in the newspaper and in the news magazines (see following section) can you find the depth of coverage you need to stay informed.

▶ ▶ ▶ Complete these activities.

3.37   Businesses pay a newspaper to print _____ as a way of telling people about their products and services.

3.38   Clever drawings that carry a political message are called a. _____ and are usually found on the b. _____ .

3.39   An advice column called "Dear Abby" appears in many papers every day; therefore, it should be called a _____ feature.

3.40   A short item about melting icebergs is probably a _____ .

3.41   If you want to know about the weather or the baseball standings, you would look at a type of information known as _____ .

3.42   Explain why many adults believe that they can be fully informed about world affairs only if they read a newspaper every day. _____

_____

_____

READING THE NEWS MAGAZINES

News magazines are an important addition to the newspaper. More specialized in content and more often directed to special interest groups as well as to the general public, they play a complementary role in keeping people well informed about life around them.

Most magazines appeal to a particular type of reader. Surfing magazines, women's magazines, sports magazines, and others specialize in stories and features about the special interests they represent. Three major magazines that sell millions of copies every week specialize in news. *Time*, *Newsweek*, and *U.S. News & World Report* are all known as *news magazines*. These magazines and a few similar ones review the major happenings of the week along with detailed background information. They also print special summaries of events in the arts, medicine, science, religion, sports, and other topics. News magazines print news of the United States as well as of world affairs. They do not normally cover events in smaller towns or everyday happenings. If a large meteorite does land in your backyard, however, you might make the cover of *Time*.

Just as few people read a newspaper from front to back, most readers do not read all the articles in a news magazine every week. More commonly, they choose those areas in which they are most interested or in which important events have taken place. Unlike newspapers, the news magazines do not usually print editorials. Each magazine does represent a particular point of view, however, and the writing is often slanted in that direction. Major articles carry a byline just as you've seen in the newspaper.

If you walk past a newsstand, you will also spot some specialized news magazines. *People* and *Us* deal with the lives of celebrities in the news; *Business Week* summarizes the week's business happenings, and *Sports Illustrated* does the same thing for the world of sports.

Students with class assignments to research current events topics find the news magazines to be excellent sources. To assist you in finding what *Time* or *Newsweek* printed on some current topic—smog control, for example—most libraries have two resources that can help you zero in on the articles you need. The older resource is a publication called *The Reader's Guide to Periodical Literature*. New editions of the guide come out almost monthly, then are printed in larger volumes by the year. This source will give you all the information you need, to find the articles you want: title, author, magazine, date, and page numbers. A faster search technique takes advantage of the computer's ability to scan large databases quickly. If your library has a computerized search capability, you need only type in SMOG CONTROL, press enter, and watch a list of articles appear on the screen.

Larger libraries keep similar indexes for newspapers and more specialized magazines in the arts, science, and social studies. The magazines and newspapers themselves are often kept on *microfilm* or *microfiche*, which permits entire issues to be reduced to the size of a postcard. A librarian will show you how to use the special readers required by the microfilm or microfiche. Some machines can even make photocopies of individual pages when you need them.

Complete these statements.

3.43 The three major news magazines are a. _____ , b._____ , and c. _____ .

3.44 If you need more coverage on business news than *Newsweek* provides, you might try a specialized news magazine such as _____ .

3.45 To find what the popular magazines have printed on the subject of religious education, look in the _____ .

3.46 Because of storage and space problems, many magazines kept in libraries today are stored on a. _____ or b. _____ .

USING NONFICTION RESOURCE MATERIALS

The following guidelines will help you make efficient use of nonfiction resource materials. You will not need to follow every rule every time you pick up a magazine. Becoming a well informed, careful reader can contribute greatly to your becoming a productive Christian citizen.

1. Work hard at becoming a regular reader. Your goal should be to read a daily newspaper and a weekly news magazine on a regular basis.
2. Keep an open mind about what you read. Remember that much of what is printed is propaganda designed to persuade you to follow a particular viewpoint.
3. Evaluate the type of publication you are reading. Does it clearly label what is news and what is opinion? Do you find evidence of slanting? Does the publisher promote a particular political or social cause?
4. Check to see who wrote the article. Some writers become known as promoters of particular points of view.
5. Compare the article with others on the same topic. Do the various sources agree or disagree? A few newspapers tend to print information (such as Big Foot stories) that no other publication picks up. That should tell you something.

6. Does the article use facts and statistics logically? Analyze such material before you accept the conclusions based upon it.

By using these six rules, you can expand your own knowledge without blindly trusting everything you see in print. The next time someone tells you that flying saucers are real, you will remember to ask for proof!

Complete this activity.

3.47 Pick up a copy of your local newspaper. Make a chart that shows the number of column inches (a column inch equals a single newspaper column wide by one inch deep) the paper devotes to (a) local news; (b) national and international news; (c) editorial opinion; (d) religious news; (e) sports; (f) entertainment—art, music, movies, books; (g) features—comics, syndicated columns, recipes, and the like; (h) society news and gossip; (i) filler material; and (j) advertising. Do you think the balance is a fair one? Write a paragraph about your findings and what you think should be changed.

Teacher check _____

Initial   Date

SPELLING

Study these words from Spelling Words-3. Learning to spell and use these words correctly will help you.

┌─────────────────── **Spelling Words -3** ───────────────────┐

all right	kidnapped	epitaph
attention	mother-in-law	eugenics
bicycle	occasion	extraneous
calendar	plaid	gregarious
copies	probably	hydraulic
despair	rhetoric	restaurant
dolphin	spoonfuls	inhibition
facial	therefore	intervene
government	twine	nausea
height	who's	occasionally

└──┘

Complete this activity.

3.48 Using a separate sheet of paper, choose twenty of these words and write a sentence for each word. When you finish, give the sentences to your teacher for checking.

Teacher check _____

Initial   Date

Ask your teacher to give you a practice spelling test of Spelling Words -3. Restudy the words you missed.

Before you take this last Self Test, you may want to do one or more of these self checks.

1. _____ Read the objectives. See if you can do them.
2. _____ Restudy the material related to any objectives that you cannot do.
3. _____ Use the SQ3R study procedure to review the material:

    a. **S**can the sections.

    b. **Q**uestion yourself again (review the questions you wrote initially).

    c. **R**ead to answer your questions.

    d. **R**ecite the answers to yourself.

    e. **R**eview areas you did not understand.

4. _____ Review all vocabulary, activities, and Self Tests, writing a correct answer for every wrong answer.

SELF TEST 3

Answer *true* **or** *false* (each answer, 1 point).

3.01	_____	Not everything you read is true.
3.02	_____	All propaganda is bad.
3.03	_____	Statistics are numbers that give reliable facts that you can always trust.
3.04	_____	An eyewitness report is a primary source of information.
3.05	_____	A newspaper article that expresses an opinion is called tabulated material.
3.06	_____	The paragraphs in a personal letter are not indented.
3.07	_____	You may write a business letter on personal stationery.
3.08	_____	Good listeners pay more attention to the speaker than to themselves.
3.09	_____	A speaker's tone of voice may tell as much as the words.
3.010	_____	Exaggeration is an example of nonverbal language.

Match these items (each answer, 2 points).

3.011	_____ _Halley's Bible Handbook_	a. byline
3.012	_____ a nationally known cartoon	b. wire service
3.013	_____ AP or Reuters	c. general sources
3.014	_____ newspapers, radio, television, magazines	d. secondary sources
		e. slanting
3.015	_____ the name of a reporter who wrote a news story appears in it	f. editorial
		g. letters to the editor
3.016	_____ short, humorous, or informative new articles	h. syndicated feature
		i. media
3.017	_____ history textbooks	j. tabulated material
3.018	_____ news article that expresses an opinion	k. fillers
3.019	_____ news article that "sells" an idea	
3.020	_____ weather report	

Complete these statements (each answer, 3 points).

3.021 _Dear Sir_: is an example of a _____ .

3.022 The date a letter is written is indicated in the _____ .

3.023 _Sincerely yours_, is an example of a _____ .

3.024 The paragraphs of a letter are called the _____ .

3.025 The name and address of the person to whom a letter is sent is called the

_____ .

3.026 The process of sorting out important and unimportant sounds is called

_____ .

3.027 Words that do not have hidden meanings are said to have _____ meanings.

3.028 Words that do have hidden meanings are said to have _____

_____ meanings.

3.029 Body posture, facial expressions, and gestures are forms of _____

_____ communication.

3.030 Similes, metaphors, exaggeration, and irony are examples of _____

_____ .

Answer these questions (each answer, 5 points).

3.031 What are three types of business letters? _____

_____

3.032 What are the three types of personal letters? _____

_____

_____

3.033   What are the characteristics of a good listener? _____

_____

_____

_____

_____

_____

_____

3.034   What parts do the business letter and personal letter have in common?

_____

_____

Complete these lists (each part, 2 points).

3.035   List three major news magazines.

a. _____

b. _____

c. _____

3.036   List four types of sources for information.

a. _____

b. _____

c. _____

d. _____

3.037   List the five *W*'s and one *H* of a news story.

a. _____

b. _____

c. _____

d. _____

e. _____

f. _____

85 / 106

Score _____
Teacher check _____
      Initial   Date

Take your spelling test of Spelling Words -3.

Before taking the LIFEPAC Test, you may want to do one or more of these self checks.

1. _____   Read the objectives. See if you can do them.
2. _____   Restudy the material related to any objectives that you cannot do.
3. _____   Use the SQ3R study procedure to review the material.
4. _____   Review activities, Self Tests, and LIFEPAC vocabulary words.
5. _____   Restudy areas of weakness indicated by the last Self Test.